SHILOH

by
Phyllis Reynolds Naylor

Student Packet

Written by
Phyllis A. Green

Contains masters for:

1	Anticipation Guide
1	Study Guide
1	Using Dialogue
1	Dog Center
3	"What Is Your Character" Poem Activity
1	Dog Writing Prompts
1	Investigate the Author
1	Vocabulary Challenge Words
1	Vocabulary Puzzle Page
1	Colloquialisms
1	Comprehension Quiz — After Chapters 1-5
1	Comprehension Quiz — After Chapters 6-10
1	Final Examination
1	Essay Protocol

PLUS   Detailed Answer Key

Note

The text used to prepare this guide was the Dell Yearling paperback edition. The page references may differ in other editions.

Please note: Please assess the appropriateness of this book for the age level and maturity of your students prior to reading and discussing it with your class.

ISBN 1-56137-606-X

Copyright infringement is a violation of Federal Law.

© 2000 by Novel Units, Inc., Bulverde, Texas. All rights reserved. No part of this publication may be reproduced, translated, stored in a retrieval system, or transmitted in any way or by any means (electronic, mechanical, photocopying, recording, or otherwise) without prior written permission from Novel Units, Inc.

Photocopying of student worksheets by a classroom teacher at a non-profit school who has purchased this publication for his/her own class is permissible. Reproduction of any part of this publication for an entire school or for a school system, by for-profit institutions and tutoring centers, or for commercial sale is strictly prohibited.

Novel Units is a registered trademark of Novel Units, Inc. Printed in the United States of America.

To order, contact your local school supply store, or—
Novel Units, Inc.
P.O. Box 97
Bulverde, TX 78163-0097

Web site: www.educyberstor.com

Anticipation Guide

Directions: Prior to reading *Shiloh*, react to the following statements, indicating whether you agree or disagree. After reading the book, return to these statements and assess them again. Explain your reactions in a short paragraph, explaining particularly any changes of opinion.

	Before Reading	After Reading
1. Property rights are sacred; no one can be denied what (s)he owns.	_____	_____
2. There is no such thing as a white lie.	_____	_____
3. Always respect your elders.	_____	_____
4. Every child should have his/her own room.	_____	_____
5. Abusers have usually been abused themselves.	_____	_____
6. It's impossible to learn to get along with your enemies.	_____	_____

Name_____

Study Guide

Directions: These questions are provided to assist the reader to understand the literal details of the book. A few opinion questions are also included. Your teacher will direct you in responding to the questions:

1. Write out short answers.

2. Be prepared to answer orally.

3. Make notes to enable small group discussion.

4. Preview the questions prior to reading a section.

Chapter 1, Pages 11-18
1. How does the author get the reader into the story?

2. What is the point-of-view of the story?

3. Identify the setting of the story.

4. What is the place of guns in the Shiloh story?

5. Who is Shiloh?

Chapter 2, Pages 19-27
1. How do Ma and Pa react to Shiloh?

2. What is Marty's feeling about Shiloh?

3. How does Marty feel about Judd Travers as Shiloh's owner?

Chapter 3, Pages 28-36
1. What does the conflict or problem in the story seem to be?

2. What is the Preston attitude about money? Cite examples from the book to support your conclusion.

3. How does Judd treat his dogs?

Chapter 4, Pages 37-45
1. What is Marty's dad's advice about Shiloh?

2. What is a game warden?

3. Explain this sentence from the book. "There aren't many leftover scraps of anything in our house."

4. How does Marty come to sleep a full night at the end of Chapter 4?

Chapter 5, Pages 46-54
1. What problems does Marty deal with in Chapter 5?

2. What lies does Marty tell in this chapter?

3. What do you learn about Judd Travers in this chapter?

Chapter 6, Pages 55-65
1. What happened after Marty ate Dara Lynn's chocolate rabbit's ear?

2. Why did Marty think so much about what he'd said to Judd Travers about the missing dog?

3. What other lies does Marty tell?

4. What kind of a childhood did Judd Travers have?

Chapter 7, Pages 66-73
1. How are David Howard's home and family different from Marty's?

2. What things did Marty do in Chapter 7 which could embarrass his parents if they knew?

3. How does Marty store his food for Shiloh?

Chapter 8, Pages 74-80
1. How does Marty feel as this chapter progresses?

2. What do these details have in common: Judd asks to hunt on the Preston land, food left for Mr. Preston by those on his mail route, friends offering headache remedies to Mrs. Preston?

3. Who discovers Shiloh?

Chapter 9, Pages 81-88
1. What alerted Ma to investigate Marty's actions?

2. What is the deal that Marty makes with Ma?

3. What ideas does Marty entertain to solve his Shiloh dilemma?

4.   Why does Shiloh awaken the family by his yelping?

Chapter 10, Pages 89-95
1.   How does Marty's dad react to discovering Shiloh in Marty's pen?

2.   Why does Ray Preston say, "We'll pay..." when he takes Shiloh to Doc Murphy?

3.   How do Marty and his dad disagree in their views about the proper handling of Shiloh?

Chapter 11, Pages 96-104
1.   Why does Marty address David Howard by his full name in this chapter?

2.   How does Marty feel after telling David about Shiloh?

3.   How does Shiloh react when he returns from Doc Murphy's care?

Chapter 12, Pages 105-12
1.   How does each of the family members react to Shiloh?

2.   Why don't Ma and Pa mention Shiloh by name?

3. What was the *"rap, rap, rap"* on page 109?

4. What is Judd's ultimatum to the Prestons?

Chapter 13, Pages 113-119
1. What is Marty's dilemma as the chapter starts?

2. What does Marty decide to do about Shiloh?

3. What is Judd doing when Marty goes to see him?

Chapter 14, Pages 120-128
1. What happens when Judd rushes from the trees to see his deer?

2. Why does Marty go against his upbringing not to talk back to grown folks?

3. What is the trade Marty proposes to Judd Travers?

4. What is the bargain recorded on a grocery sack?

Chapter 15, Pages 129-144

1. Why does the family "about pet Shiloh to death" in this chapter?

2. How does it go with Marty working for Judd Travers?

3. How does Judd try to "break" Marty?

4. How does the story end?

Using Dialogue

Directions: Choose a bit of dialogue from the book to investigate. Fill in the chart to describe this way of writing and telling a story.

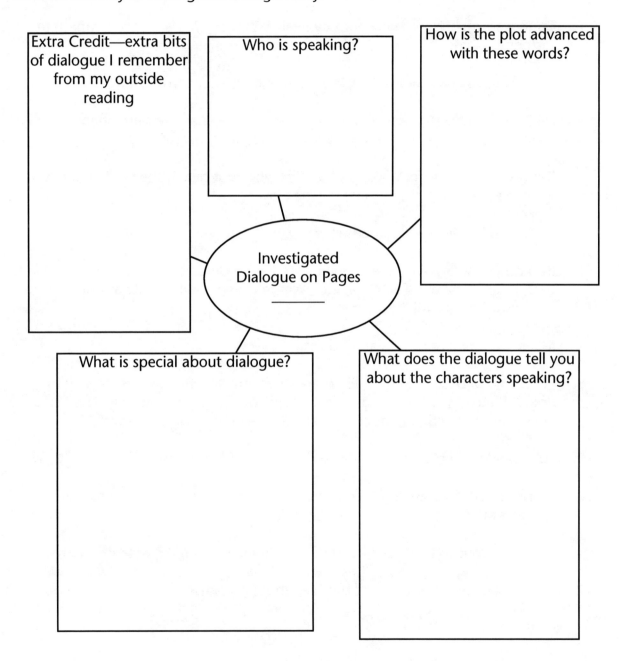

Extra Credit—extra bits of dialogue I remember from my outside reading

Who is speaking?

How is the plot advanced with these words?

Investigated Dialogue on Pages _____

What is special about dialogue?

What does the dialogue tell you about the characters speaking?

Dog Center

Directions: Choose one of these dog activities. Display your work for class members or other school classes.

1. Famous Dogs — How many dogs can you list that have been made famous in cartoons, TV, movies, songs, or books?

2. How do dogs communicate? Write an imaginary dog conversation.

3. Fables are fictitious stories that teach a lesson. The characters are often animals. Try writing a fable with a dog as the main character.

4. Design a dog game for dogs to play. Describe your game, the rules, and any materials necessary so the game can be played.

5. Design an imaginary "dog house."

6. Be a dog for a day. What would you do? How would you feel? What would you eat? Decide on your size, color, etc. Where would you live? What will be on your mind? What will you fear?

7. Make up several dog jokes and riddles.

8. What kind of people do dogs like? Are there any animals that are friendly to dogs? Pretend you are a dog. What people or animals do you associate with? Share your tale with friends and discuss their reactions to your story.

9. How would school be different if students brought along their dogs?

10. Promote your favorite dog breed or mixed breed. Prepare an advertisement, oral or written.

11. Compare dogs to two other kinds of pets. Prepare a graphic organizer to report.

12. If dogs could talk, what would they say about humans?

"What Is Your Character" Poem

Directions: Write as though you are the main character in the book. In the first line name two special characteristics of your main character. In the second line, name something your character is curious about. Continue following the directions for each line of the poem. You will need to be creative; you may need to go beyond what the book's author tells you directly in the story.

_____ Is
(character name)

_____   is   _____
(character name)   (two special characteristics)

_____   wonders   _____
(character name)   (something the character is curious about)

_____   hears   _____
(character name)   (an imaginary sound)

_____   sees   _____
(character name)   (an imaginary sight)

_____   wants   _____
(character name)   (an actual desire)

_____   is   _____
(character name)   (the first line of the poem repeated)

"What Is Your Character" Poem — Stage Two

Directions: Building on the first stage description of the book's main character, continue by creating more details in a second stanza.

_____ pretends   _____
(character name)   (two special characteristics)

_____ feels   _____
(character name)   (a feeling about something imaginary)

_____ touches   _____
(character name)   (an imaginary touch)

_____ worries   _____
(character name)   (something that really bothers the character)

_____ cries   _____
(character name)   (something that makes the character very sad)

_____ is   _____
(character name)   (the first line of the poem repeated)

"What Is Your Character" Poem — Stage Three

Directions: Building on the first two stanzas, continue by creating more details in a third stanza.

_____ understands   _____
(character name)   (something the character knows is true)

_____ says   _____
(character name)   (something the character believes in)

_____ dreams   _____
(character name)   (something the character dreams about)

_____ tries   _____
(character name)   (something the character makes an effort about)

_____ hopes   _____
(character name)   (something the character hopes for)

_____ is   _____
(character name)   (the first line of the poem repeated)

Writing Prompts

Directions: Respond to these writing prompts as your teacher suggests; writing for a specified amount of time or writing a specified length.

- The first day I had my dog …

- The funniest thing my dog ever did …

- My dog likes to …

- Write from a dog's viewpoint:
    - What does it do while owner is at school or work?

    - What does it think about?

    - What are its likes and dislikes?

- The best dog story I've read is …

- The weirdest dog (or pet) on a television program or in a movie was …

- My favorite dog names are … because …

- Dogs make the best pets because …

- I'd never choose a dog as a pet because …

- Dogs are really smart. (Give reasons to support your supposition.)

Investigate the Author

Directions: Investigate your book's author. Fill in this mini-interview. Once you've exhausted the materials available at the library, make up the rest of the answers. Mark your made-up answers.

Name _____

Education _____

Hobbies outside of writing _____

Family _____

_____

Travel favorites _____

Best loved books as a youngster _____

_____

Best advice given to the author_____

_____

Best advice given by the author _____

_____

Future plans _____

_____

Vocabulary Challenge Words

Directions: Look over the following list of words from the book, as you read each chapter. Put a check if you know the word for sure and a star if you've seen the word but aren't sure of its meaning. Locate and note the location of the words in the book; record a definition for the words you don't know ("unstarred" and "unchecked")—your first challenge. Your second challenge is to become sure of the meaning of the starred words.

Chapter	Word	Mark	Definition
1	groveling		
	whimper		
	cringe		
	whopping		
	ford		
	gristmill		
2	loping		
	yelps		

Vocabulary Challenge Words—Page 2

Chapter	Words	Mark	Definition
3	cases		
	froggy		
	sickle		
4	warden		
	feeble		
	shadbush		
5	nourish		
6	devilment		
7	whooping		
	yowls		
8	gunnysacks		
9	suspicions		
	mistreat		
	yelp		
	snarl		
	bawling		

Vocabulary Challenge Words—Page 3

Chapter	Words	Mark	Definition
10	wince		
	stethoscope		
11	warble		
	antibiotics		
12	shrieks		
	slurp		
	decency		
13	allergic		
	rehearsed		
14	camouflage		
	warden		
	weirdest		
	intention		
	slogs		
	regulation		
	allowance		

Vocabulary Challenge Words—Page 4

Chapter	Words	Mark	Definition
15	omission		
	jubilation		
	squaller		
	whetstone		

Vocabulary Puzzle Page

Directions: Fill in each puzzle piece with as many examples of what is requested as you can.

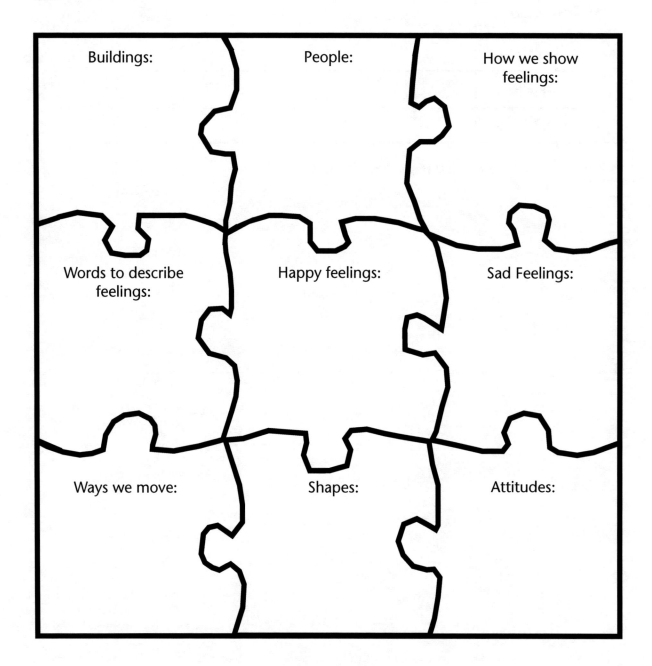

Buildings:

People:

How we show feelings:

Words to describe feelings:

Happy feelings:

Sad Feelings:

Ways we move:

Shapes:

Attitudes:

Colloquialisms and Interesting Language from the Book

Directions: Colloquial expressions are informal conversational or speech patterns particular to a certain region. Locate the following expressions in the book. From context clues, figure out what each expression means, filling in the chart below.

Chapter	Expression	Context Clue Definition	How you might express the idea today
8	"smooth as buttermilk"		
12	"patching him up"		
13	"sadness inside me"		
14	"I'm cooking now"		
14	"talk back"		
15	"...mouth so dry it feels like fur"		

Comprehension Quiz #1

Part I — Match the characters with lettered statements.

_____ 1. Judd Travers   A. Uses a wringer washing machine

_____ 2. Marty Preston   B. Named for a place

_____ 3. Ray Preston   C. Youngest Preston

_____ 4. Dara Lynn Preston   D. Lives alone

_____ 5. Becky Preston   E. Tells the story

_____ 6. Ma   F. Seven years old

_____ 7. Shiloh   G. Postal carrier

Part II — Identify these story map parts.

Setting — Place	
Setting — Time	
Conflict	
Point-of-View	

Part III — Mark these statements as true or false. If the statements are false, make corrections.

____ 1. Shiloh is elated the first time he meets Marty and runs up to lick his face, wagging his tail.

____ 2. The Preston table is bountiful; Ma prepares wonderful varied meals, always fixing much more than the family can eat.

____ 3. Ma doesn't encourage her children to keep pets.

____ 4. Marty and his father return Shiloh to Judd and Marty promises he'll keep a look out for Shiloh and return him to Judd.

____ 5. Marty builds a pen for Shiloh when the dog escapes.

Part IV — Choose three of these words to use in a sentence.

ford	cringe	whimper
shadbush	sickle	loping

Comprehension Quiz #2

Part I — Choose four of the following details from the story to identify. In a sentence or two demonstrate your understanding:

snake stick   David Howard   Mr. Wallace's corner store

food in mailboxes   squash   Doc Murphy

Baker's dog

1.

2.

3.

4.

Part II — Match these vocabulary words with appropriate meanings.

_____   1. gunnysack   A. shrill cry

_____   2. yowl   B. medical instrument used to listen
                                                to sounds in the body

_____   3. yelp   C. a plant often called the
                                                serviceberry

_____   4. snarl   D. flinch

_____   5. stethoscope   E. running with bounding steps

_____   6. wince   F. mill for grinding grain

_____   7. shadbush   G. burlap bag

_____   8. loping   H. threatening growl

_____   9. ford   I. dismal distressful cry

_____   10. gristmill   J. shallow place in a river where
                                                crossing is possible

                                        K. skipping

                                        L. bark

Final Exam

Part I — Match these words from the story with an appropriate definition.

___ 1. cringe	A.	sharpening stone
___ 2. loping	B.	joy
___ 3. shadbush	C.	shrink in fear
___ 4. yowl	D.	trill
___ 5. yelp	E.	serviceberry
___ 6. wince	F.	toils
___ 7. ford	G.	low plaintive cry
___ 8. sickle	H.	running with long strides
___ 9. warden	I.	dismal cry
___10. whimper	J.	tool with curved blade
___11. slogs	K.	draw back
___12. jubilation	L.	shallow place to cross a river
___13. squaller	M.	shrill cry
___14. whetstone	N.	scream
___15. warble	O.	public official

Part II — Using five of the building blocks below, select a character from the book to tell about.

Who is the character?

What did the character do?	Why did s/he do it?

Why is the character's name well chosen?	What is the nature of this character's actions? *(reactive, active, important, consequential, secondary)*	What is the significance of the book's time and place to the character?

What is unusual or important about the character?	How does the character change in the story?	Does the character remind you of another character from another book? Who?	Do you know anyone similar to this character?

Name_____

Part III — Choose the best answer.

1. The dog Shiloh is named for
    a) a place in the Bible
    b) Marty's grandfather
    c) the place Marty met the dog
    d) a computer game villain

2. Phyllis Reynolds Naylor got the idea for the book from
    a) her veterinarian son
    b) a dog she met while visiting friends in West Virginia
    c) a computer-generated list of ideas
    d) a dream

3. The book takes place
    a) during the summer when Marty is eleven
    b) in rural Georgia
    c) during the 1930s
    d) in rural Virginia

4. The plot of the story heats up when
    a) Judd reports the loss of his dog to the sheriff
    b) another dog attacks and injures Shiloh
    c) Marty's dad apologizes to Judd and returns the dog
    d) Marty runs away from home

5. Marty starts his deception
    a) when he avoids telling Judd that he has Shiloh
    b) when he sees Judd's treatment of his dogs and secretly releases the pack
    c) when he realizes that his family won't help him
    d) when he is scolded for being lazy

6. Which of the following is **not** one of Marty's ideas to resolve his problem about Shiloh?
    a) give the dog to a stranger
    b) auction off the dog at a fair
    c) buy the dog from Judd Travers
    d) give the dog to one of his friends in town

© Novel Units, Inc.

7. Marty manages to rescue Shiloh permanently by
    a) selling his prized gun to pay Judd
    b) striking a deal with Judd
    c) reporting Judd to the game warden
    d) borrowing money to pay Judd

8. What is the main idea in the story?
    a) Abuse and neglect can be overcome.
    b) Growing up is difficult.
    c) An abused dog can never be trusted.
    d) The West Virginia mountain country is backward.

9. Marty strikes a deal with Travers by
    a) threatening him
    b) appealing to his good nature
    c) agreeing not to report Travers to the game warden
    d) offering to work 60 hours for Travers

10. Which of the following is **not** true about David Howard?
    a) He lives in town.
    b) He is Marty's older friend from church.
    c) His mother is a teacher.
    d) His father works for a newspaper.

11. Which of the following is true of Ray Preston?
    a) He's postmaster in Sistersville.
    b) His mother lives in a small cabin on his property.
    c) He is one of five children.
    d) He takes Shiloh to the doctor.

12. *Shiloh* by Phyllis Reynolds Naylor
    a) was written during the 1930s
    b) is illustrated by Garth Williams
    c) won the Newbery Medal
    d) features a terrier and a mountain family

Part IV — Essay

Directions: Choose one of the questions below and write a well-developed paragraph of response. Be sure to identify the question you are answering, and use examples from the novel to support your statements.

1. I'd like to live in West Virginia. Agree or disagree. Explain why.

2. The setting of *Shiloh* is easy for me to understand. Agree or disagree. Explain why.

3. Dog stories are the best. Why?

4. The book *Shiloh* is well-crafted. Agree or disagree. Explain why.

5. The book *Shiloh* teaches valuable lessons. Name the lesson and support your conclusion.

Answer Key

Study Guide

Chapter 1

1. Shiloh is mentioned in the first paragraph. The family is introduced through the storyteller's eyes.
2. first person; story told by Marty
3. West Virginia hills, time is contemporary
4. Guns are used to hunt. The eleven-year-old storyteller has a .22.
5. a dog that follows Marty home, named for the place he was first seen

Chapter 2

1. Ma thinks there's no extra food to feed a dog. Pa respects Judd Travers's rights as Shiloh's owner.
2. He really likes the dog and thinks it's unfair that Judd abuses the dog.
3. Marty doesn't like Judd Travers because of his past mean actions. So Marty doesn't consider Judd a good owner for the dog.

Chapter 3

1. saving Shiloh from Judd Travers
2. Money is scarce, Marty sleeps on couch in living room, no pay for babysitting, no food to keep a dog.
3. chained, keeps them half starved, no names, kicks them, no food for Shiloh while watching other dogs eat

Chapter 4

1. forget about Shiloh, put your mind to other things
2. The game warden is a government officer who makes sure that the laws for hunting are obeyed.
3. The Prestons have very little extra money because they contribute to Grandma Preston's care.
4. Shiloh has run away to Marty and Marty has built a pen for Shiloh.

Chapter 5

1. feeding Shiloh and answering Judd Travers's questions about his missing dog
2. Page 47, what he did during the day. Page 48, he's not hungry at mealtimes and wants to eat later. Page 50, going off to practice his aim with his .22. Page 53, answers to Judd.
3. He's suspicious about Marty. He doesn't respect the hunting laws.

Chapter 6

1. Dara Lynn threw a fit, Marty denied eating it and Ma told Marty Jesus knew who ate the candy. Marty finally confessed to Dara Lynn.
2. Marty knew he'd lied by avoiding the truth and he felt guilty.

3. about getting the food he needs to feed Shiloh, about David Howard, about snakes, about returning Shiloh to Judd Travers
4. abusive

Chapter 7
1. The Howards live in town in a big house. David's mother is a teacher and joins the boys for lunch.
2. He accepts a lot of food from Mrs. Howard and asks Mr. Wallace, the store owner, for cheap old cheese or meat.
3. in an old H-C can with plastic wrap over the top in the stream with a rock on top to keep out raccoons

Chapter 8
1. apprehensive, worried about Shiloh being found
2. all are a result of Marty's keeping Shiloh
3. Ma

Chapter 9
1. Marty saving extra squash which he'd never liked to eat. Ma knew someone else was doing the eating.
2. Ma won't tell Marty's dad about Shiloh for the night if Marty promises not to run off.
3. Run off with the dog; give Shiloh away; take the dog to Friendly, hoping to give him to a stranger passing through.
4. Shiloh is attacked by the lone German shepherd.

Chapter 10
1. The dog has been attacked when he discovers him. Ray Preston reacts to the immediate need of the dog for medical help.
2. He wants Shiloh looked after and he feels Marty's pain. He ignores the family's lack of extra money.
3. Ray wants his son to do what's right, to go by the law. Marty wants things to be changed to protect the abused dog.

Chapter 11
1. David has found Shiloh's pen and Marty explains about Shiloh. David knows that his full name is a signal for a serious talk.
2. relieved
3. happy to be with the Preston family

Chapter 12
1. Ma pets Shiloh when she passes his box, Pa gives the dog meal scraps and scratches his back. Dara Lynn brushes the dog.
2. The author doesn't say for sure but it seems Ma and Pa know that the dog really isn't theirs and they hesitate to use his name.

3. Judd Travers knocking at the door
4. Judd wants Shiloh back by Sunday.

Chapter 13
1. how to protect Shiloh from additional abuse at the hands of Judd Travers
2. tell Judd he won't return the dog
3. shooting a doe out-of-season

Chapter 14
1. Marty walks up and accuses Judd of killing the doe out-of-season.
2. He is so angry with Judd Travers that he stands up to him.
3. Marty's silence about the doe-killing for Shiloh
4. Marty will work 20 hours for Travers. Travers will give Shiloh to Marty.

Chapter 15
1. Marty tells his family that he has made a deal with Judd to buy Shiloh.
2. Judd is nasty and requires very hard work from Marty.
3. He claims their bargain isn't right and legal because there was no witness.
4. Marty completes his half of the bargain and he owns Shiloh. Judd Travers mellows very slightly toward Marty.

These are the page numbers for the vocabulary words for Activity #9:

groveling, 13; whimper, 14; cringe, 14; whopping, 15; ford, 15; gristmill, 16; loping, 20; yelps, 27; cases, 29; froggy, 29; sickle, 34; warden, 38; feeble, 39; shadbush, 42; nourish, 48; devilment, 61; whooping, 67; yowls, 67; gunnysacks, 76; suspicions, 82; mistreat, 82; yelp, 87; snarl, 87; bawling, 88; wince, 89; stethoscope, 91; warble, 102; antibiotics, 103; shrieks, 106; slurp, 106; decency, 110; allergic, 115; rehearsed, 116; camouflage, 120; warden, 120; weirdest, 120; intention, 120; slogs, 120; regulation, 122; allowance, 122; omission, 130; jubilation, 132; squaller, 135; whetstone, 140.

Quiz #1:
Part I
1. D
2. E
3. G
4. F
5. C
6. A
7. B

Part II
    Setting — Place: West Virginia hills
    Setting — Time: Present day
    Conflict: Plight of the dog Shiloh
    Point-of-View: First person narrative

Part III
1. F   Shiloh holds back when he first meets Marty.
2. F   The Prestons have limited food resources.
3. T
4. T
5. T

Part IV — Answers vary

<u>Quiz #2</u>
Part I — Answers vary

Part II
1. G   2. I   3. A   4. H   5. B   6. D   7. C   8. E   9. J
10.F

<u>Final Exam</u>
Part I
1. C   2. H   3. E   4. I   5. M   6. K   7. L   8. J   9. O
10.G   11.F   12.B   13.N   14.A   15.D

Part II — Answers will vary. Look for students to convince you they understand the character.

Part III
1. C   2. B   3. A   4. B   5. A   6. B   7. B   8. A   9. C
10.B   11.D   12.C

Part IV — See essay evaluation form, page 36.

Essay Evaluation Form

1. **Focus:** Student writes a clear thesis and includes it in the opening paragraph.

10	8	4

2. **Organization:** The final draft reflects the assigned outline; transitions are used to link ideas.

20	16	12

3. **Support:** Adequate quotes are provided and are properly documented.

12	10	7

4. **Detail:** Each quote is explained (as if the teacher had not read the book); ideas are not redundant.

12	10	7

5. **Mechanics:** Spelling, capitalization, and usage are correct.

16	12	8

6. **Sentence Structure:** The student avoids run-ons and sentence fragments.

10	8	4

7. **Verb:** All verbs are in the correct tense; sections in which plot is summarized are in the present tense.

10	8	4

8. Total effect of the essay.

10	8	4
100	80	50

Comments:

Total: _____

(This rubric may be altered to fit the needs of a particular class. You may wish to show it to students before they write their essays. They can use it as a self-evaluation tool, and they will be aware of exactly how their essays will be graded.)

© Novel Units, Inc.